the art of breathing

the art of

breathing

frédérick leboyer

element books

By the same author

Birth Without Violence
Loving Hands
Inner Beauty, Inner Light

Original German version
Die Kunst zu Atmen
© 1983 Kösel Verlag GmbH & Co, Munich
English text © Frédérick Leboyer 1985

First published in Great Britain in 1985 by
Element Books Ltd
Longmead, Shaftesbury, Dorset

ISBN 0 906540 82 8

Printed by Wincanton Litho, Wincanton, Somerset
Jacket designed by Humphrey Stone

Photographs by Frédérick Leboyer

to
Savitri
and to
India
who both opened for me
the gates of the pulsating, sparkling
realm of sound

to
Yvonne Fitzgerald
whose feminine deep understanding
of the mysteries
of language, poetry
and birth
helped so much improve
the English version of this book

to
Pamela, Giacomella
who tested, tasted and enjoyed
this 'art of breathing'
in daily life and in labour

may many
follow in their wake

religions are many
sects numberless
yet all follow only two ways:
one takes you to knowledge
and the other to love.

reaching the goal
one discovers with surprise
that there is no knowledge
separate from love
that, truly, love is knowledge

and that the secret gate to both
is one:
the breath.

C.M. Chen

an introduction

Tell me, Socrates, can virtue be taught?

Meno

One who casually leafs through this book,
looking at the pictures might say
"A pregnant woman is having lessons,"
and so jump to the conclusion that
here is being offered
a new technique, yet another method
which will improve childbirth
make it easier, quicker, snappier.
The sensitive reader will suspect that
there is more to it than meets the eye
If mastery over one's own breath
is, indeed, so important in childbirth
it is because breath is what lies behind
all that is
at the root
of the whole Creation.

In this great battlefield we call the world
the fight seems to be everywhere
good fighting evil
day fighting night
darkness fighting light.
Two
continuously, endlessly fighting each other.
Fighting?
Meaning that one has to do away with the other
destroy it, kill it?
No! Far from it!
It is, indeed, quite the opposite.
Kill one of the dancers,
you kill the dance.
In truth, it's not a fight
but a ballet
an endless explosion of joy, of infinite energy,
of infinite love.
The moment the fight becomes bitter
aggressive, destructive
joy turns to sickness
life and love to hatred.
And death takes the road.
Always and wherever you look
two are there
action and rest
masculine, feminine

Yin and Yang
not trying to murder each other
but dancing, circling in divine embrace.
And so it is
with the two halves of one's breath!
inhale, exhale,
continuously whirling together.

But then, one might ask
why is it a woman
giving another woman
a lesson of such deep wisdom?
Well, when Socrates himself asks
"What is kindness, what is beauty, what is love?"
and can find no answer
it is to a woman, Diotima, he turns.
"Love? The thirst for beauty?
My dear Socrates, these are nothing but
driving forces
which lead to procreation
of beautiful children
in women
of works of art
in the artist.
Poetry means to give birth, to give being.
The writer, the painter, the architect,
the musician, the actor, the dancer,
the poet
all give birth, give being

give form
to what, originally, was merely in their minds.
Only after months
of slow, secret, silent growth does any work of art
all of a sudden
burst forth.
Just like children being born.''
And so,
however meaningful this book can be
for women who are with child
at heart
it's meant for all
women and men as well
for the wiseman and the fool
since only the fool
is wise enough to live
for love.
For all, but above all
for the artists, these truly mad people
heavy as they are with the beloved child
the work of art growing within.
Who seeks more the secret of
this breath
than these tragic lovers
distracted as they are
by their longing, their thirsting

for the divine
inspiration
to animate, breathe life
into their passionate creation?

But then
can 'it' be taught?
Breathing lessons?
That sounds like a joke.
Is not breathing going on all day
all night
whether we are aware of it or not?
Yet, yes
it can be taught
rather made free, full, deep.
So deep that in the end
you touch the root.
Just as one progresses from crawling on all fours
through standing, walking, running
to dancing,
one can go
from grunting and groaning
to talking and singing
then to poetry, to chanting
and thus, possibly, some day taste the ultimate.

And so now
lovers of life
thirsting for joy, for breath
let's meet and watch these two women
young in their years
old in wisdom
since it is the perennial privilege of their sex
to drink from the very fount
and know that the secret spring
of the whole Creation
is love
expressing secretly, endlessly,
through the breath.

I

letting go?

– Dear me, Giacomella, what's the matter with you?

– Nothing. I am just relaxing.

– Relaxing? You're collapsing.
  What's wrong with you? Are you ill?

– No. Just a little tired.

– A little? Is it all too much for you?

– Oh, Pamela, to tell you the truth, all my courage
  has gone. And so has all my energy.

– So close to the birth of your child? How could that be?

– I feel so weak, so unhappy. I don't even know how I'm
  going to be able to manage.

– And is this why you're trying to relax?

– Yes. Everybody says that relaxation is the answer.

– And does this collapsing really help you?

– Oh, no. I even feel that the little courage I still
  had deserts me.

– But this is absurd. You ought to be full of tranquil,
  lasting energy, full of a secret joy.

– I wish I were.

– Then, come on. Pull yourself together.

5

My poor Giacomella!
The way you are sitting now is
even worse.
Now you are so stiff, so rigid.
Do you really think you could hold on like that
for long?
— No. You're right. I certainly couldn't.
— Then, I beg you, just let go.

From bad to worse.

Dear me, if you could see yourself now, you'd get a shock.

You look like the village idiot.

— But, what am I to do!

For heaven's sake, what am I to do!

— Certainly not react as you did.

Reaction is never the answer.

— No?

— It merely takes you from one extreme to the other.

Only to let you down in the end.

Yes, in the end, you're no better off
than this poor man,
who looks just as miserable and worried as you.
– But, then, what am I to do?
– What to do?
   A good question.
– Oh, I think I know.
   I ought to be sitting on the ground.
– On the ground?
   I'm not sure I quite follow you.
– But, Pamela, I have been doing meditation for years.
– Yes?
– And we've always been taught meditation sitting
   on the ground.
– Well, if you feel that would help you, try.
   I don't want to impose anything on you.
   I'm only here to help you.

2

posture
imposture?

– See?
   Isn't that much better?
– My dear, my sweet Giacomella,
   don't be offended. You know that I only want to help you.
   You don't mind if I tell you the truth?
– No. Please tell me.
– Well, the truth is that
   no
   that's not it either.
   You look like a child who's done something wrong
   waiting for the punishment.

– Then what about
   that?
– I'm terribly sorry, but it's no better.
– But why?
– Can't you feel that you're stiff all over.
   You seem to be saying
   I'm not guilty! I'm somebody!
   But it's not true.
   It's not
   you.
   It's all artificial, it's all made up.
   Just be yourself.
   Do relax, do let go.

17

Oh dear!
The moment you let go,
the village idiot is there again.
I am afraid you'll have to accept that
sitting on the ground
or what you took to be meditation
never really helped you.

– Now I'm totally lost.
   Of course, you make me see that relaxation hasn't
   helped me at all.
– Don't blame relaxation! It's only that you are
   not relaxing.
   You're collapsing.
   And such a passive attitude will never help anyone.
– But surely relaxation is passive.
– Oh, no!
   And yet, it's difficult to explain.
   It's passive, yes.
   But it's an active passivity.
– An active ... passivity? Surely that's a contradiction.
– No. A paradox.
   As for 'active passivity' it simply means that
   although you are not doing anything
   yet you are very alert.
   You're not thinking of something else.
   Your mind is not wandering,
   'thinking' about this or that.
   You're fully here
   just like a cat
   about to pounce.
– I'm afraid I don't quite follow you.
– Because you're trying to understand purely by thinking
   with your head.
   Like our poor friend, the thinker.
– The more you tell me, the more you confuse me.
– And yet, it's so simple.
   Maybe I can help you to see.
– I wish you would.
– Alright. Let us try.

21

3

sit up straight!

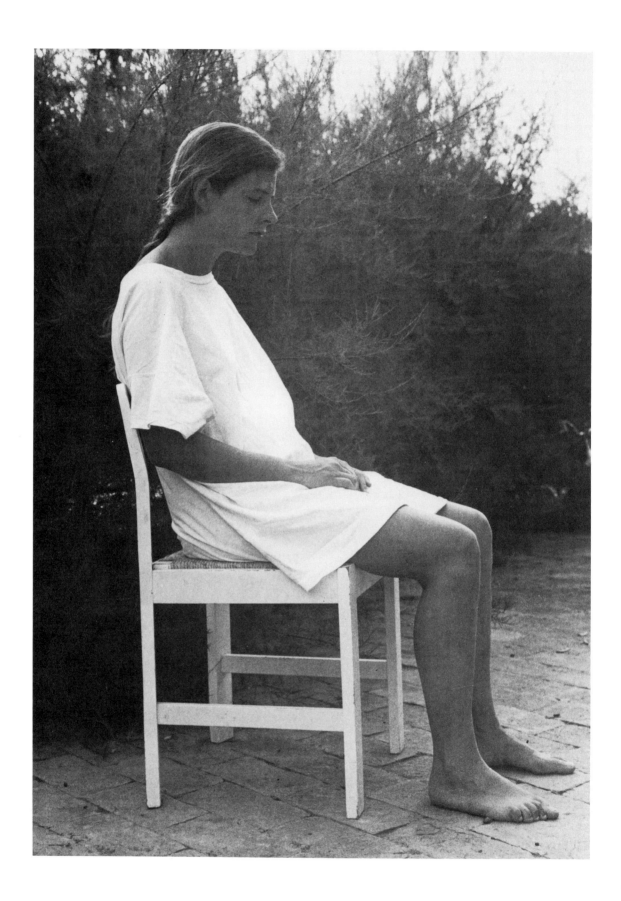

From
the drawing-room
down to
the lounge . . .

– Giacomella,
  can you see it is not
  this?
– Of course.
  Did I really look like that?
  Now, you too look like an idiot.
– If this is relaxation,
  no, thank you, not for me! Don't you agree?
– Now I'm feeling ashamed of myself.
  Just as you said
  no, thank you, not for me!

– And it's not
    this either.
    Why?
    Because there's no freedom
    no peace and no tranquillity here.
    I'm sure you can feel that
    this is the child
    the poor, terrified child, once again
    startled and reacting with a jerk
    to the all too familiar
    "Sit up straight!"
    Of course you sat up straight
    out of sheer panic
    jolted by such an electric shock
    with so much anger, so much fear in the air
    how could you not be paralysed, petrified!

27

I suppose you're beginning to see that, whether you
collapse, or become as stiff as a poker, it is always
the child in you,
it's your past.
It has nothing to do with your muscles, with your body.
It is an attitude that built up long ago.
And what is it that tells me
that there's no freedom, no peace, no joy in you?
– I don't know.
– Really? Well then, I am going to tell you. It's so simple.
There's no breathing in you.
Or so little and so superficial, so inhibited,
so timid, so shy.
– I'm afraid you're right. And so, that is the secret?
– Yes. When you're afraid, you tense and
hold your breath, don't you?
– That's true.
– This is what you started doing years and years ago,
when you were still a child or even a baby.
And, although the root is in the distant past
the effect is still here, now:
you're paralysed, you're stuck.
Therefore what is wanted is to get your freedom back.
Freedom meaning the freedom,
the fullness of your breath.

– Now I can see why everyone puts so much emphasis on breathing,
  why we are taught breathing exercises.
– Exercises? Exercises can never make you free. No
  more than laughing can be learnt. Or innocence, or
  spontaneity.
  I'm afraid all your teachers can think of is
  'plenty of air for the baby'.
  Which is never going to solve *your* problem.
  Which is never going to help *you*.
  And, it's you, first of all, we want to make free.
  The joy, the happiness of your child, primarily
  is your happiness, your joy, your freedom.
– So I won't have to do these terrible exercises?
  I'm so glad! What a relief!
  To tell you the truth, one of the things that worried
  me so much was that, far from helping me, these breathing
  exercises we are taught made me feel terribly confused.
  For one thing they are so difficult to practise.
  They seem to me to be so unnatural.
  And then, worse still, they make me feel so tired.
  Even, at times, my head goes empty and I begin to
  feel dizzy.
  So that I was asking myself
  if I feel so bad about them now
  how are they going to help me when I'm really in
  trouble, when I'm in labour!

30

In fact, from what friends who've had babies told me,
most of the time they didn't even work. And that
was really dreadful.
Feeling that all they had so earnestly learned
had let them down, they were furious.
Toppling from such high hopes, how could they not
feel cheated, frustrated, bitter.
Anger, even more than pain, was gnawing at their
hearts.
— That's all very sad indeed.
So, as you see, we have, first of all,
to make this point of breathing very clear.
But, before I tell you anything, you tell me
what you are taught.
— Well, we have several exercises.
To begin with: panting.
It's a kind of fast, superficial way of breathing
we are supposed to do before we can push.
And, actually it's very hard to do. This is the
kind of breathing that makes me feel dizzy.
— And then?
— Then we are taught to push.
— How are you to push?
— We are told to take in as much air as we can,
hold it
and push.
— Oh! Is this really what they teach you?
My goodness, this is not at all the way!

– No?
– No. And then, what else are you taught?
– That's all.
– No. Really? If I follow you, panting before you're
   allowed to push and taking in plenty of air, holding
   it in, and pushing?
   I suppose you can see that this is all about what they
   so poetically call the last stage of labour, pushing
   the baby out.
   But what about the beginning?
   How are you to temper the contractions, tame the
   fierce waves that keep surging one after the other
   for hours and hours?
– We are told to relax.
– To relax? Excellent. How?
– I don't know. They don't tell us anything.
   They say we must relax.
– You *must*? How absurd. As good as telling
   a poor man who's in despair that he *must* laugh.
   How can you relax if you are not told
   how?
   Can you open a door, a safe, if you're not given
   the key, the secret?
– So, there is a secret?
– Yes.
– But then why aren't we told!
– Your teachers, probably, do not know.
   As for the secret, as I'm sure you suspect
   it's breathing.

– To keep breathing? That's all there is to it?
– To keep breathing, yes. But in a very special, very
   precise way. Again, listen carefully:
   the secret of relaxation is
   a long, even out breath,
   letting the air out very slowly
   until you have emptied yourself completely.
– Letting the air *out*? Why! This is just the
   opposite to what we are taught!
– When you are tense, you hold your breath, don't you?
– That's true.
– Any strong emotional situation comes to an end, finds
   its relief, its 're-solution' either in laughter
   or in tears: crying, sobbing?
– True.
– Both are exhaling, letting the air out, aren't they?
– Why of course!
– But such uncontrolled explosions, although they do
   relieve the tensions, leave you with your battery
   empty. Simply because you've been exhaling from your
   chest, where all your emotions are stored up.
   Once you are free from these emotions that come
   from your past, which are truly your past, the road
   is free for true breathing:
   not from the chest but from the stomach.
   And this stomach breathing is the second secret.
– Is it? But . . . again, this is just the contrary
   of what we are taught!

33

They keep telling us to take in air with our chest.
– Really! But why?
– So that we do not disturb the baby.
– But that's completely wrong.
  We've already agreed that the happiness of your child
  is, first of all, *your* happiness, your freedom.
  And chest breathing, being very superficial can
  never give you peace and tranquillity.
  Free, right, full breathing is filling up from
  the stomach.
  That's the way children and babies breathe.
  And the reason why they overflow with joy, with
  energy.
  It is this full breathing you have lost and must
  recapture.
  When you put an empty bottle under a tap,
  it fills up from the bottom, doesn't it?
– Of course. You're right. And, yes, stomach breathing
  is the way children, babies breathe.
  And so, stomach breathing is the other great secret?
– Yes.
– But since you said that breathing can no more be
  taught than innocence or laughter,
  how is one to learn this stomach breathing?
– You don't learn it. You re-learn it, recapture it.
  Rather, you make it free.
– But how?
– The secret is very simple: you sing.

35

– Sing! Oh, but I can't! I could never, never . . .
– How do you know?
– I never could. I'm much too shy. And, when I was a child
   and I used to sing, "Oh, please, shut up! Your voice is
   really dreadful!" would immediately thunder and
   silence me. And, anyway, as you know
   "Children should be seen and not heard."
– I know. Our so-called education.
   But singing is the only way. So, please, try.
– But, I told you, I can't. I'm stuck.
– Stuck? Try to see where.
– In my stomach, in my throat.
– Now we are making progress.
   The pit of the stomach, the throat, that's where
   the knots are, where the fears are lying, dormant.
– Please, don't press me. Or you'll make me cry.
– And what of it? The tears you've suppressed
   for so long, would make you free
   the moment you let them flow.
   And so, now, come on.
   Just try.
   Open your mouth
   and sing with me
   this very simple sound
   'ah'.

37

– See!
I told you. I can't. I can't.
– Of course, you can.
You are perfectly in tune.
Your ear is good, which is most important.
Simply there is no strength in your singing, no energy.
– Really?
You're not just trying to be nice to me?
– No. I'm not.
Your voice is weak, there is no life in your singing
because you are blowing with your chest.
And as I told you this is precisely what one is not
to do.
– Then, please, teach me.
Now I feel we are really getting somewhere.
Will you teach me?
– Gladly.
And I can promise you:
you will be free.

4

the trap

– I am going to show you all your mistakes.
And, of course, you know I'm not laughing at
you. I'm only trying to help you, make you see
how, unconsciously, you choke yourself.
Look at me. I'll show you what you do.
When asked to sing, you take in air first . . .
– Of course I do. How else could I sing?
– When I ask you a question and you answer me,
do you take in some air first?
– Well . . . no.
– You just open your mouth and answer, don't you?
– I'm afraid you're right.
– Then, even worse, in order to take in air
you do the most terrible things:
you arch your back,
raise your shoulders, tensing your neck,
and stick your chest out.
– That's what everyone does when they take a deep breath.

– Oh, oh!
  Take a deep breath?
  For one thing, we agreed that there is no need to
  'take in air' to answer a question, didn't we?
– Yes. You're right.
– And then, sticking your chest out and creating a
  void, you possibly snatch in some air.
  Very little, actually.
  This is not breathing, my dear Giacomella.
  This is gasping.
  The proof that you really achieved nothing with
  this very poor show?
  The moment you sing you let go
  and collapse.
  Why?
  Tensing your back, your neck, your shoulders
  you've put yourself in jail.
  Can you see, can you feel that I am tense to the
  very tips of my fingers?
  I'm so miserable in this straight . . . jacket
  that all I want is to get rid of it all,
  get rid of the tensions
  and of the air
  all bottled up together.

47

What a relief.
But what a disaster.
Those who've got eyes
but cannot see
might say:
"How touching.
Doesn't she look sweet?"
They don't realise
that you're drowning
that it's all leaking out
with your energy vanishing
and that, like a punctured tyre,
you'll soon end up
flat, finished, empty.

49

Flat, finished and empty.
A very wrong understanding of being relaxed.
Relaxation, although passive is a very active state.
Passive and quiet you are, but yet vibrant and intense.
Then what is the cause of this terrible confusion?
You committed all the major sins:
arching your back
tensing your neck, raising your shoulders.
taking in air with your chest.
– But that's what everyone does when they're taking
a deep breath.
– Taking a deep breath?
Never!
There is only giving, emptying.
Air will come in,
as a response.
It will happen. It can't be your doing.
– Now, I understand.
And so, one shouldn't take in plenty of air?
– Never.
Right, full breathing is no more
pumping in plenty of air
than relaxation
is collapsing.

5

the art of breathing

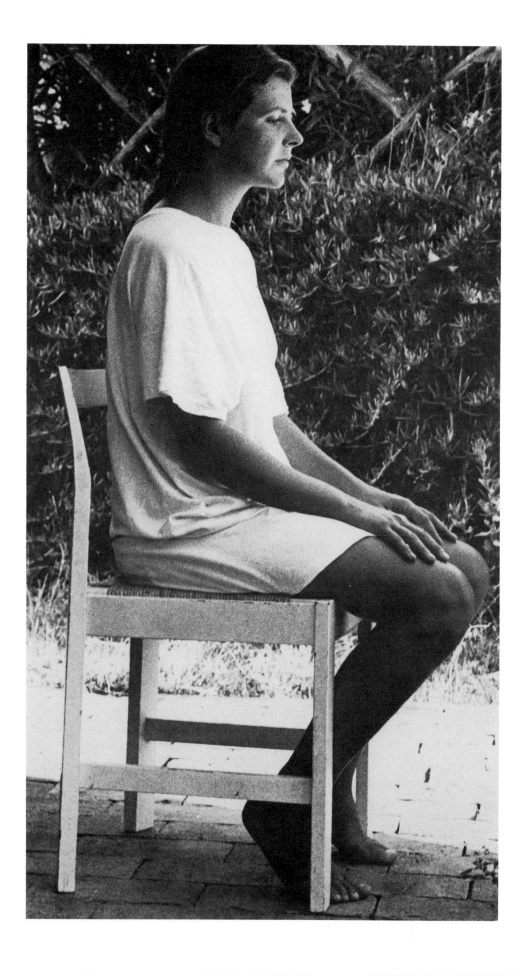

*"Before you can run, you must walk.
Before you walk, you stand.
Before you stand, you sit."*

– I am afraid we've been very negative until now,
talking mostly about what to avoid, what not to do.
But then, you don't pour new wine into a dirty bottle.
You wash it out first, don't you?
And so, now, let's learn how to sit.
Once you can sit, Giacomella,
once you can sit on a chair properly,
there is nothing beyond your reach.
– Are you serious?
– Of course. If your sitting is right
your breathing is automatically full and free.
And, tell me, what more do you want!
How do you reach this perfection?
By altering, correcting this or that? No.
You are to take your body as a whole,
move it sideways, to the right, to the left,
to and fro as if rocking it very gently
until two signs will tell you that it's right
that you have found your centre, your axis:
your shoulders will drop spontaneously
and, mostly, you'll become aware
that there's breathing in your stomach.
By the way, tell me,
is your stomach breathing now, is it free?

55

– Breathing . . . my stomach? I don't know.
– Oh, Giacomella!
– How could my stomach be breathing?
  The lungs, not the stomach . . .
– Giacomella! Now, come on. An intelligent girl like you.
  The point is that, actually you don't feel your stomach
  and you don't feel it because you don't want to.
  It's a part of your body, or rather it's a part
  of yourself you're trying to ignore.
  Now, tell me, can you feel your baby?
– Oh, yes. It keeps moving all the time.
  So much so that I can't sleep.
– Moving, kicking? That's not what I'm talking about.
  Do you feel that *someone* is there?
  Can you feel this baby's joy?
– Its . . . joy?
– Well, I'm afraid you don't.
  If this joy, this energy had reached you,
  you would never feel so down, so depressed.
  The sad fact is that you are not actually
  with this child.
  It is a guest you have not truly accepted
  and welcomed.
  But let's come back to your sitting.

57

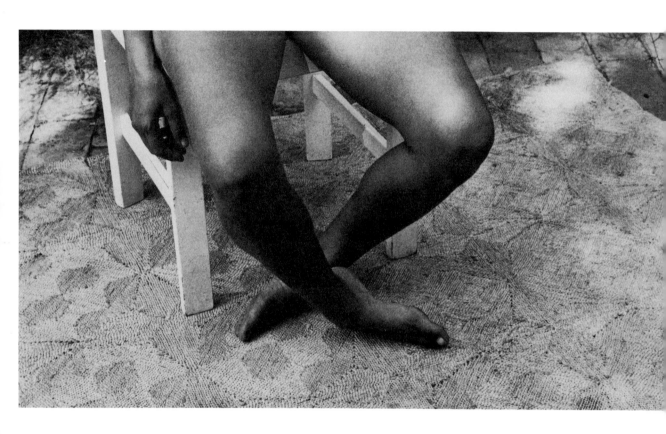

Before we go any further, one or two points.
Details, as you may know, are all important.
Your knees.
Education taught you to keep them tightly closed.
You'll have to learn to let go,
give up this unconscious defensive attitude.
But not with feet like this.

58

You are no more aware of your feet
than you are of your stomach.
Although they are your roots.
The very anchor of your fragile vessel.
Keep them alive.
And sensitive.
Let them feel the ground for you.

59

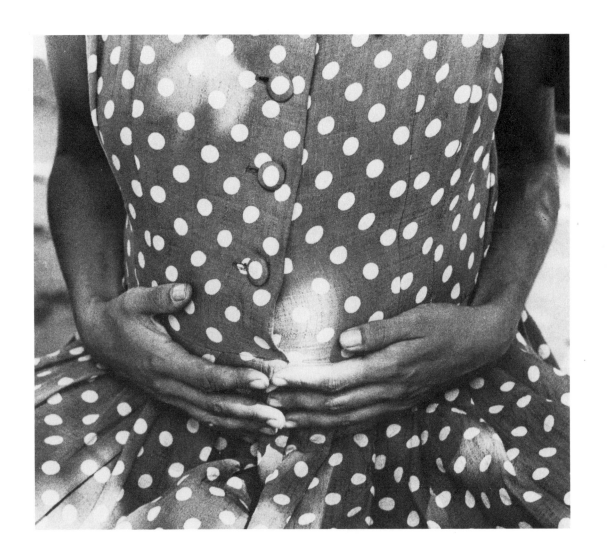

And, now, let's go back to your stomach.
– Pamela, you know you make me feel uneasy.
   There are things I find difficult to talk about.
– Whether you want to discuss them or not they are facts.
   And it's a fact, you've got a stomach.
   To try to deny it, ignore it, well it's foolish.
   I am afraid you'll have to accept it. Simply
   because it is there.
   And since, indeed, you're not aware of it
   since you simply cannot feel it from inside
   as being truly part of you
   you'll have to rediscover it from outside.
   Don't be afraid! Don't jump!
   It's all very simple.
   Just put both your hands underneath your stomach.
   Keep these hands very, very light and sensitive.
   Let them feel. Let them feel and follow.
   Feel what?
   Your own shyness, first of all.
   And then, that nothing is moving in this part of
   your body.
   There's no breathing.
   It's stuck, paralysed, ignored, non-existent.
   It's dead!
   It's a part of yourself
   you don't want to know anything about. Why?
   Fear.
   This is why this part of you cannot let go.

Now, let's bring it back to life.
Look at me and follow very carefully.
I put my right hand
on the front of my stomach, well below the navel
and my left hand,
the back of my left hand, you notice,
against the lower part of my back.
Now, watch my hands:
see how, the moment I bend my head,
relaxing the nape of my neck
without in any way altering anything in my back
yes, see
how slowly, spontaneously
my stomach begins to move and fill up.
Can you see
how it begins to expand, pushing my right hand forwards?
And can you see that it is
not my doing,
that it merely happens
of its own accord?

Now,
only now,
now that my stomach,
not my chest,
now that my stomach is full
am I ready to sing
and breathe out.
Not just letting the air out
or trying to get rid of it as quickly as I can,
and crying and laughing are nothing else,
but blowing very, very gently,
lovingly.
Can you see how my stomach is moving, emptying?
Can you see my right hand following the movement?
Following, mind you!
My hand is not pressing, pushing.
And neither am I moving my body, my muscles.
I am truly singing and sound,
yes, sound is directing everything
while my sensitive hand is merely sensing, following,
flowing with the breath.

Now, I am empty, my stomach is empty.
My two hands are so close to one another
that they almost touch as it were.
I am at the end of my wits, at the end of my breath.
The natural reaction at this point, the reflex
would be to take in air right away
in order to stop the panic.
And this, I would do with my chest:
snatching some air, not much,
to quieten the anguish.
But I don't.
I know better.
If only for a second or two
I remain empty.
I have the courage to wait
to taste this emptiness, this void.
And that, really, changes everything.

When I let go
not as a reaction but of my own accord
my stomach,
not my chest,
begins to fill up.
And how long, how deep, how full,
how refreshing, exhilarating
this long, spontaneous inward breath.
It fills me up to the top.
Simply because it started in the right place:
at the bottom.
Like the empty bottle under the tap,
you remember?

Full and free.
Vibrant with energy.
How extraordinary the joy that wells up
from the depths
of my Self!

Now, will you try?
– Yes.
– See!
   the moment your hands
   are in touch with your stomach
   and you begin to feel,
   everything changes.
   You are straight
   but not tight
   your shoulders are relaxed
   your head, your back
   your sitting
   are all perfect!

73

One of the secrets, you see,
is in the neck.
The moment you let your head drop slightly
as if looking at your knees
there is a spontaneous letting go.
And everything, in you, falls into place.
Because you're free
your stomach begins to fill up.
You can feel it pushing your hands apart, can't you?

75

Now,
without, first, taking in air,
and why should you, now that your stomach is full?
Without, first, doing anything
just as you are
as if, simply, opening your mouth to answer a question
sing this deep, this long 'ah'.
And all the time, keep your eyes
which is to say, your mind
on your hands.
You are, as it were, breathing out through your hands!
Feel how perfectly breath and movement are flowing
together.
Steadily, go to the very end.
Stop when the sound begins to waver.
Stop and, for a second or two
remain empty.
Only after you have tasted this void
let go.
And see, or rather, feel
how the air rushes in
making your stomach expand, making it full
and then filling up your whole being!
Emptying, emptying . . .
and, because empty, completely empty
then, suddenly
completely full!

77

– Now, I can't talk.
   It's so strong, so deep,
   the effect is so extraordinary . . .
   and yet, it is all so simple.
   I couldn't express in words
   the tranquillity, the peace, the silence
   and yet the energy, the joy.
– Don't try.
– And . . . my child is so quiet.
   I think, for the first time.
   So quiet and . . . so happy.
   I can feel it in quite a different way.
   And now I understand what you meant.
– All that, simply because you had the courage
   to wait, to remain empty
   and taste this void.
– A whole part of myself
   which must have been dead for so long
   has come back to life.
   A desert, a miserable dried up land
   at last revisited by the rain
   in flower again.

79

— If you could just see the way you're sitting now!
  Every part, in you, is free and right.
  Your head is right
  your shoulders free.
  Simply looking at you, one can even feel
  how your hands are light, relaxed.
  No arrogance, almost a humility and yet
  what dignity.
  Perfect simplicity
  and yet you look like a princess.
  Just for a few minutes more, don't talk.
  Don't spoil the joy.
  Just be there
  with the blessed emptiness
  the bottomless silence.

81

— This big, obvious stomach
which was so difficult to accept
which I pretended to ignore
now at last
is part of me.
It is, indeed, my deepest, dearest
most precious me
my Self.

83

6

heaven and earth

Before quarrelling with the world,
check inside!

Sheik Amir Abdull

– Although you weren't moving much
   haven't you come a long way?
   Now, you can sit on a chair, can't you?
   The world is yours
   and you can attempt anything
   even sitting right on the floor. Sitting on the ground
   seems very much the thing to do
   now that people look so much to the East.
   And what a mess they make of it.
   See! Look at me
   and now, of course, you can't miss
   the chin stuck forward
   the nape of the neck that's locked
   the general collapse
   the eyes that look nowhere, the lack of energy,
   the sadness, the misery, the emptiness
   and the suppressed anger.
   Freedom? There is none. And no breathing either.
   And why?
   It takes three points, for anything to be able to stand.
   Where can you find them, here
   with knees like this, just hanging in the air?

87

This is a completely different story isn't it?
— As different
  as night from day!

Oh but Pamela,
it seems as if you're about to take off
and fly
soaring higher and higher!
And yet, at the same time
it's the image of a big tree
that comes to my mind.
A great, glorious, majestic tree
rooting ever
deeper and deeper.

– Shall I tell you one more secret, dear Giacomella?
  You sit on a cushion.
  Yes, it's as simple as that.
  You see, it changes your centre of gravity.
  And that, changes everything.
  Spontaneously, your shoulders drop,
  effortlessly your knees
  come to rest firmly on the ground.
  Haven't you now your three points?
  With such solid foundations
  what could ever shake this mansion?

Spine, back, knees?
No.
There is much more to it than that.
What?
Accept that it is a great mystery.
Between your hands you can feel
something
moving, flowing
which you cannot describe
which the Chinese, the Japanese call *ki,*
the Hindus, *prana*
and our mystics 'grace'.
And, do you know?
It is this mysterious 'something'
which makes the bullfighter hold his hand to his back
so that he can remain unmoved, steadfast
while he plays with death.
And it is the same fire
that keeps the Flamenco people
dancing like mad devils
until the break of day!

95

What is this fire, this energy,
this passion
with which you seem to overflow
turned, as you are, into a fountain,
a spring?
Again, no one can tell.
Call it joy.
Or life.
No. Call it love
since it is all one.

And, yet, beware.
It is not yours.
You are merely a channel.
It flows through you.
You can open to it
not command it.
If you expect it will obey
your sweet will
you're in for a serious disappointment.
Therefore, remain modest, you are only
an instrument.

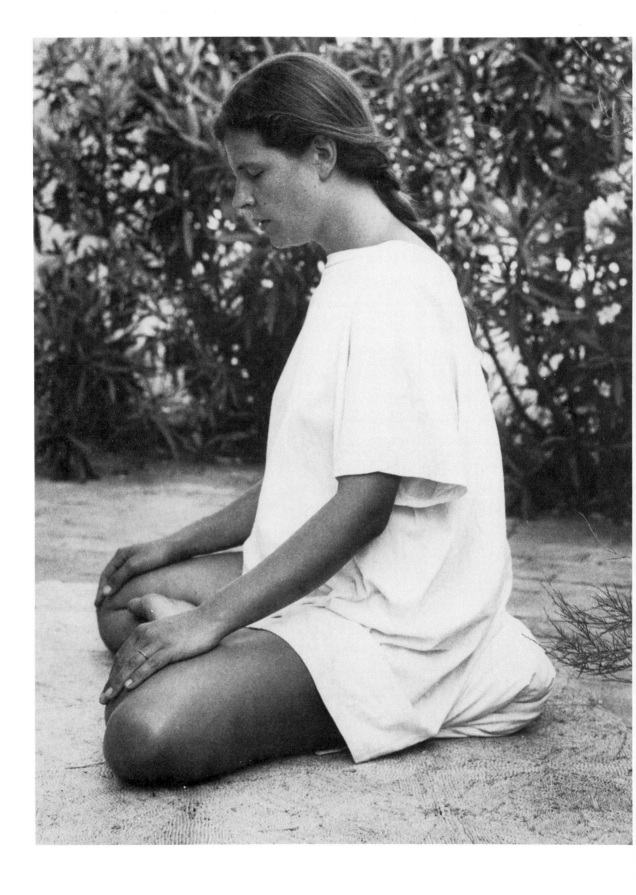

And never forget,
this is another paradox,
that it all begins
in silence
just as movement is born
out of stillness.

Shall I tell you another great secret?
The most hidden, the innermost tensions
are in the nape of the neck.
Keep it free and
all is free.
Just see
without altering in any way your now perfect back
let your head drop
until your chin meets your chest.
And feel, enjoy
the refreshing, immense breathing
that wave of the great sea
that runs, rushes through you, opens your back
and makes you vast, empty
as peaceful and quiet as the great Earth.
And, by the way,
when we started talking about all this
you said,
"Why are you asking me to look downwards?
If one is drawn to the spiritual, shouldn't one
turn one's eyes and thoughts upwards,
towards the skies, the heavens?"
Strange that things really work
just the other way round
just the opposite of what we think.

7

the art of meditation

Who are you?
Nobody. I am.
Nobody? Is that your name?
No.
Then, what's your name?
I told you.
I am.

Homer *The Odyssey*

– Giacomella, now it's your turn. You try.
– Like this?
– No, no!
  What's the matter?
  You're stiff again. You look so uncertain.
  You're trying too hard. Relax!
  And worst of all, you're trying yet again
  with your head.
  Remember 'the thinker', that poor fellow
  who will never, never get an answer?
  You too, now, are thinking!
– I'm thinking?
– Yes! How do I know?
  By your eyes
  which are nowhere,
  telling me that, once again,
  you are not 'here and now' in what you are doing
  but, once again, 'in your mind'!

107

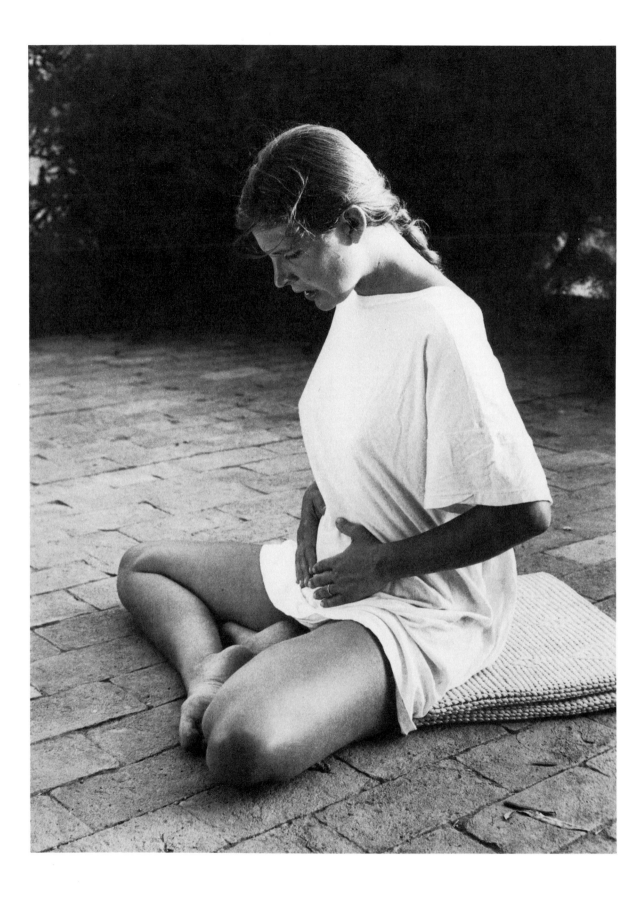

Then . . . all right
let us go back
let's start again from the beginning.
Put your hands,
both your hands, this time
against the lower part of your stomach
and while you keep your eyes on them
start breathing out through these hands of yours.

– Like this?
– You're asking me!
  Can *I* tell you what you're feeling?
  How long will you keep expecting
  answers from outside?
  Just go inside.
  Look inside.
  And don't forget,
  relax your neck.

Ah, yes, now you've got it.
How wonderful that the moment your head is right
everything falls into place.
Now every part is
right
in its own place
as it should be.
And the moment it is right
everything opens up
and you feel free.

Feeling, sensing
and flowing with the breath.
Can you feel
your stomach moving, expanding,
coming back to life again?
Can you feel your hands being pushed apart?
And can you feel
yourself
overflowing
full and fulfilled?

And, once again don't forget!
It is not an exercise
something you do
with your stomach, with your body.
You are singing, chanting.
And all that matters
is the sound.
This sound which, like a seed
begins to sprout
and, effortlessly, irresistibly
begins to grow.

All that matters, with this sound
is its beauty.
And beautiful it is
when right
true
perfect: neither too low
nor too high
in its own place
at the very level it should be.
And not only is it pleasing to the ear
but full
vibrant with joy
with life's infinite energy.
Coming from the right place in you
it resonates
awakening its harmonics
just as, at the caress of dawn
the forest awakens and quivers
with all its birds madly chippering, twittering
while the Earth vibrates in ecstasy.

Pleasing to the ear
and even more so
to the heart.
Only your heart
can tell
since only your heart
will know.

Now put your hands
back on your knees.
Rest.

Feel and enjoy
this state of non-doing.
See how full it is.
Taste the strength and the joy
that well up from nowhere
surging from that bottomless silence
out of that void.

8

cross roads

Jubilate!
Exultate!

— As always,
  there are two possibilities,
  there are two ways.
  One takes you to sorrow.
  It is a very, very ancient road,
  the cult of suffering,
  the worship of pain and despair.
  Its roots are lost in time immemorial.
  Its song?
  "In pain shall ye give birth
  Mater Dolorosa."

131

When breathing is so wrong
that instead of making you full,
overflowing . . .

. . . it lets you down, leaves you flat,
finished, empty,
this is exactly where you will land.

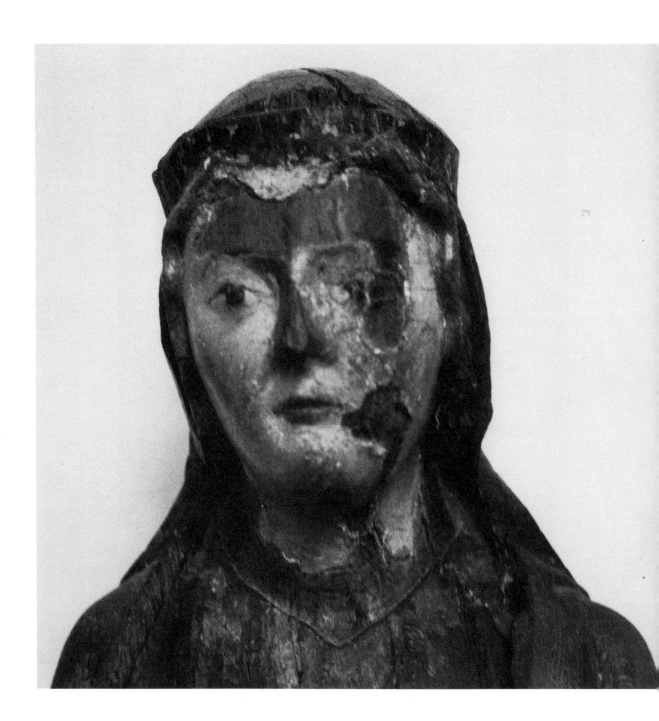

If it concerned only
you
one might say
"What of it?"
But this sadness, this despair
which comes from your mother
who got it from her mother
who inherited it from your great-grandmother,
this mountain of sorrow which has been building up
from one generation to the next
since the beginning of time
why
why should one child
your child
carry this mass of misery, this load
on his poor weak shoulders?
Why should this little one
carry this cross all through his life?
For truly, he'll feel guilty
punish himself and pay
for a harm he'll think he's done to you
while all the time it was for you
to turn this so called misery into sheer ecstasy.

Then, for heaven's sake
for this child's sake
turn the pain into joy
leave the sad way behind you!

137

Not pain
but energy
warmth
joy
endless, boundless
light and love!

Don't fight! Don't resist!
You know, now, what keeps
the gate open:
your breath
your voice.
Keep everything open
let yourself be flooded
and swept away in sheer ecstasy!

141

9

the art of breathing
the art of sitting

Once it has been fully disciplined
the breath follows its Master.
Discreet, tender,
faithful as a lover
as light and gentle as a child's whisper
and yet, at times,
all powerful, quick, astounding
like a flash of lightning!

Toriki San

— All I could give you, I have given you.
  All that could be told, I have told you.
  Now you know the one secret
  how to use the breath
  or, rather, how to flow with it
  and let it carry you.
  Yes, you know the difficult secret of relaxation,
  letting go
  a long, long, protracted out breath
  active and firm all along, although very gentle
  the perfection of which expresses in the quality,
  the stability, the beauty
  of the sound it produces.
  Stable and beautiful
  and with clear limits
  so that, although truly it takes place, it happens,
  yet you are the master.

144

You don't let it fade away, die away.
As soon as it becomes unsteady,
begins to wobble, to waver,
you stop!
And then, you have the courage to remain there
empty
and taste this void
out of which when 'you' let go
an inward breath is born spontaneously
as a response, a reward
making you full beyond expectation.
Exhale, exhale, is the secret
although, after a while,
exhale, inhale will begin to alternate
as in a dance
when rhythm, the real lord,
takes command.

What else do you learn
in Zazen from a true Zen teacher
what else in meditation
or in any of the Martial Arts?

Active, passive,
masculine, feminine,
yin and yang
exhaling, inhaling.

Exhaling, letting the air out, giving
that's yang, that's masculine
while taking the air in, inhaling
that's yin, that's feminine.

The moment giving
has got the upper hand on taking
you know the great secret
that truly opens the gate.

Masculine, feminine?
Does it mean that man is stronger than woman?
No!
They're made to dance together.
Truth is that
child is taking
and adult is giving.

146

And this is the deep, the great, the dramatic
transformation in you, dear child.
As a maiden
what else did you know but taking, getting?
While now, as a mother
your warmth, your milk
your thoughts, your smiles,
your love
your time
you'll be giving endlessly
so that, although by nature
you are water
you become like the Lord, the Sun,
the eternal giver.

And then, one more lesson you've learnt,
patience.
Patience that conquers time,
time, the lord of all.
Very few, indeed, have the courage you had
to wait
unaffected, unmoved, unshaken
when in deep water, in difficulty, in trouble.

– May I ask one more question?

– Of course, please do.

– This breathing, which I'm now beginning to
understand better, which I've tasted, how shall
I use it when I'm in labour?

– I'm glad you're asking that.
Any knowledge which is not born of personal experience
or cannot be put into practice is empty.
But before we go into practical details which I shall
be only too glad to give you,
since as you now know we are not talking about
a merely physical exercise, something you do with
the body,
but truly a discovery of your deeper Self, tasting
another level, another dimension of the Mind,
let me tell you a parable, let me tell you about
the storm.

– The storm?

– You see, the whole experience, rather the adventure,
of giving birth, and of being born, since
both are one and the same,
yes, the whole adventure is like the Odyssey:
a long perilous journey towards home through the storm.

– I'm not sure I really follow you.

– A journey into the unknown. A terrible tempest.
As I'm sure you know, you can tell that labour
has started because your stomach becomes tense.
You are having a contraction.

Another one follows.
Then another.
But 'contraction', 'stomach', 'pain', no. These are
not the words you should use.
They point to the body.
While you are there no more.
They are misleading, indeed, since they take you
the wrong way.
They make you miss the depth, the magnitude of the
experience, of the journey.
You are aware, of course, of how powerful words are.
Therefore, 'contractions', 'pains', 'stomach', no.
Don't use these words.
Paint quite a different picture in your mind.
Think of waves, of a storm you are sailing through.
And aren't these 'contractions' which come, subside
only to be followed by others bigger and bigger, longer
and longer, are they not, actually, like waves?
– So it seems. And, indeed, I like the picture.
– Waves galloping one after another, waves of the
all mighty sea of life, of infinite energy.
An energy which, of course, frightens you since never
before have you experienced it in that way.
And because you are terrified by the intensity, you
tend to withdraw, you try to stop it, fight it, while
the weak little boat that you are is tossed this way and that.

150

– What a beautiful, a fascinating description.
  I never thought of it like that.
– Caught in a storm.
  And you all at once the boat, the captain and
  the sea!
  Now the question is:
  what will the captain do?
  Well, at times, in that fit of madness which can
  turn the bravest into a coward, the poor captain
  deserts the deck and the wheel.
  He runs down to his cabin, closes the portholes fast,
  puts wax in his ears, and begins to scream his head
  off hysterically.
  His whole attitude is saying that he won't have anything
  to do with the storm.
  Although it is there of course.
  And tell me, by ignoring, trying to deny the storm,
  is he going to save his boat?
– Of course not. It will end up on the rocks.
– Shipwreck and disaster.
  It's when you are in deep waters that you want the
  captain on deck, isn't it?
  And so now the only thing to do is *to be there*, eyes
  wide open, fully aware of all that's going on.
  A light and sensitive hand on the helm, like any good
  skipper you respond to the slightest impulse of the
  sea, of the wind, of . . . your breath and thus keep your
  boat afloat, on course.
– I've been sailing myself. I've been caught in storms
  and I know what you mean.

Truly you make me see
what's written between the lines.
And so, the wind is my breath and
I
am all at once the sea, the storm, the boat ...
And, the mast, is my spine?
– How well you understand everything.
– How great, how truly extraordinary to look at it
like that.
You make me really long for that storm.

152

– Mind you, the power, the energy of the great sea
    is frightening.
    It's not for nothing it's called the Almighty.
    Once it's lost its temper you feel you are nothing:
    at this point, the boat is nowhere.
    It makes the bravest shudder and turn pale.
    And this giving birth, this giving passage to a child
    into this world is a terrible test. You're put on
    your mettle.
– I am ready. I will face it.
– That's what I expected from you.
    And, anyway, wouldn't you rather be told the truth
    and know what's in store for you?
    I feel sorry for women who expect that they're in for a
    'mild', a 'soft', a 'nice' experience.
    It's dreadful to think how they've been deluded by
    words they wanted to take the wrong way.
    'Painless childbirth', 'birth without violence',
    this they took to mean that delivery could be 'sweet
    as honey', or even that they could go through the
    adventure without even feeling anything!
    As if a tidal wave or an earthquake could be 'nice
    and sweet' or go unnoticed!
– Yes, it is absurd.
    You know, you really make me yearn for that storm.
    The taste of salt is on my tongue.
    I can feel the spindrift. The intoxication is in
    my heart.
    To get drunk . . . drunk with the fury of the sea,
    the sea of joy, of love,
    to get drunk with the ecstasy of infinite energy!

153

– How well you understand now.
   But once again, let me tell you: it's a terrible
   test.
   Life and Death,
   the face of Life in its fullness,
   the face of Death
   which is more frightening?
   And how fine a line between the two.
– Death?
– Yes, indeed. You die, as it were. Or, rather,
   something dies in you. Where is the boat? Where is . . . you?
   And the moment you die, you are reborn afresh.
   As steel through fire, then through water, is tempered,
   you are transformed and born anew.
– No wonder there is so much fear.
– As for 'acceptance', 'letting go', 'surrender', now
   you understand that neither is it passivity nor blind
   absent-minded acceptance.
   You cannot ignore the storm, deny it.
   No more than you can stop it.
– Ignore it? Never.
– Such a great adventure is only for the brave.
   And they are very few.
   But you are one of them.
   Therefore I can enlighten you, tell you
   how to sail through the storm.
   And so, now, listen carefully.

Now you are in labour.
A wave rises and then subsides.
Another one follows.
– And I begin to concentrate?
– To concentrate?

What do you mean 'concentrate'?
– This is what we are taught.
– Concentrate on what?
– Anything. Whatever we like. On a tree we see through
    the window, a picture on the wall.
– Is this really what you are taught?
– Yes. We are told that, since the mind cannot be in
    two places at the same time, since the pain is inside,
    in the body, the moment we concentrate outside, we
    won't feel the pain.
– Not feel! So that's what you want? You want to
    miss the adventure, desert the deck, run down to your
    cabin?
    To concentrate on something else! My goodness!
    When you are in the arms of your beloved, do you
    try to keep your mind somewhere else? Do you
    turn on the television or start reading a magazine?
– Well . . . this is what we are taught. But, to miss
    the storm, to miss the ecstasy, that is absurd.
– You are not to concentrate. And, certainly, not
    to concentrate on anything 'outside'.
    Concentration is narrow, petty, restricted.
    You are to be aware.
    And awareness is wide open, all inclusive.
    With concentration you see only the helm of your boat.
    And thus miss the magnitude, the beauty of the storm.
    In awareness, on the contrary, you see all
    the helm
    and the storm!

157

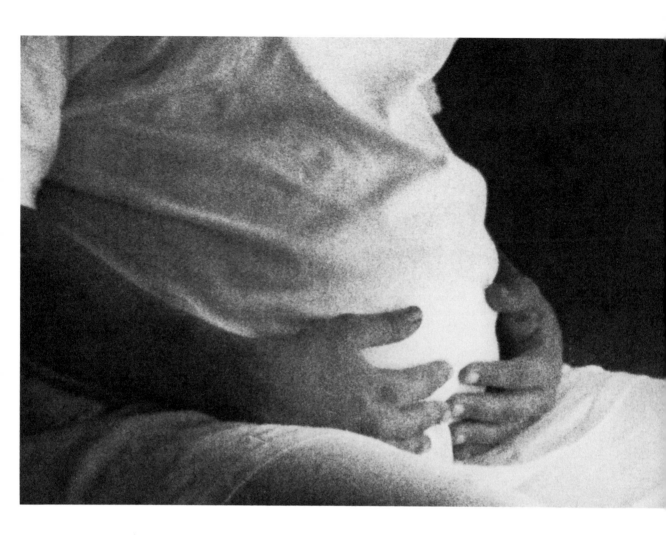

As for ignoring the contraction? No, no!
How can you pierce its secret
unless you are fully with it, one with it?
Fighting the contraction? That is to say
tensing all over and holding your breath?
No. No more can you stop the storm!
Then, how to be one with it, flow with it?
My dear Giacomella, it is all so simple.
A contraction begins. Just as you did in your singing
practice, you put your hands on your stomach, feel
its movement and, as your hands are moving towards
one another
you keep exhaling slowly, firmly although very gently.
As for the beauty, the music of the sound
that comes out of you, it tells
that contraction and breathing harmonise perfectly.

158

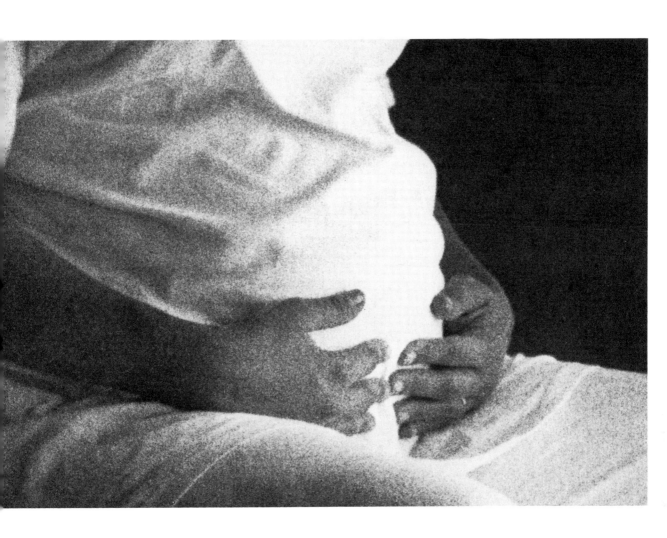

Now the contraction is at its peak.
Your hands are so close to each other that your
fingers touch.
At which point you find yourself at the end of your
breath,
empty!
This is the crucial point at which your mastery will
show,
where you are going to reap the fruits of your
patient, loving practice.

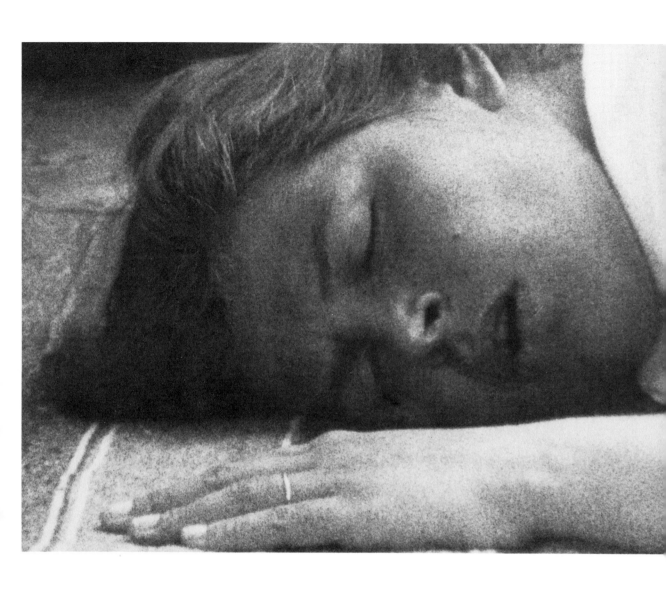

As I was telling you, the contraction is at its peak
and you are at the end of your breath,
empty.
The feeling is one of great uneasiness.
Very close to panic.
And the temptation is to bring it to an end,
to take in air right away.
Since your stomach is still in the grip of the contraction,
what else can you do but take in air with your chest?
But since this is completely wrong as you now well know,
since it is untimely,
instead of relief it brings pain
so much so that the next moment, you breathe out this
air violently:
you scream.
Now you have entered a terrible and vicious circle.
Instead of flowing with the contraction, instead of
being in tune with it,
you fight it and since you're now out of tune, you've
lost the beat.
The moment you struggle, you suffer.
And so you try again in panic, to take in some air,
again in the wrong way only to reject it violently
as if to get rid of the contraction and the pain.
And this you would keep doing endlessly
with the pain increasing continuously.
The more you suffer, the more you scream
and suffer
and scream ...

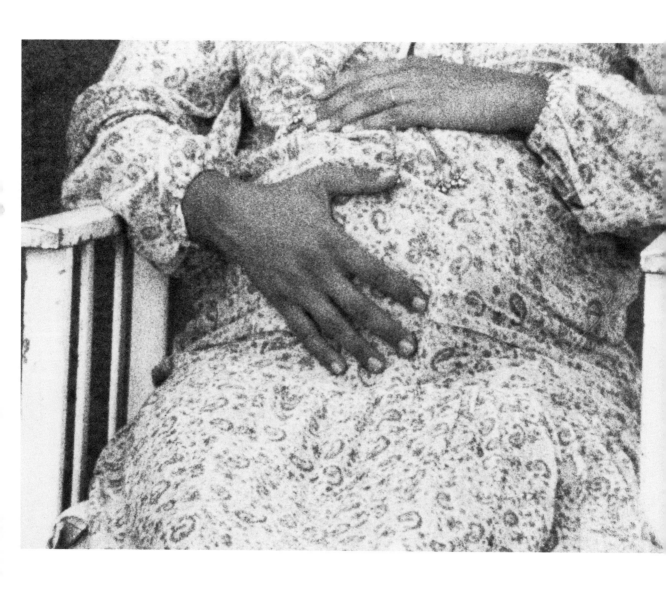

Thank God, you know better.
You do not fall into the trap.
You know that the one thing is
to keep in tune with the contraction,
never to find yourself off the beat.
And so you have courage. You have patience, wisdom.
And you wait.
You have the courage to remain empty
until the contraction comes to its end.

162

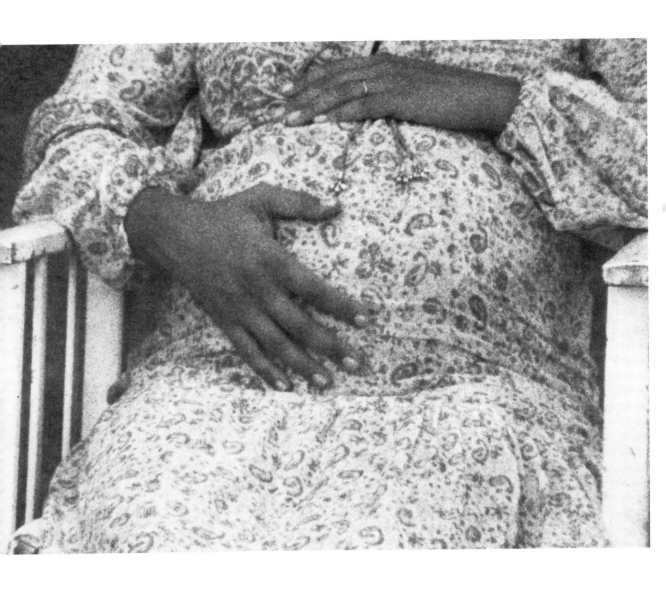

And it does!
Your hands can feel your stomach relaxing,
expanding.
Now, and only now, as your hands are being
pushed apart,
you inhale.
Or, rather, no.
You simply let the air in.
And how it rushes in, filling you up from the bottom
to the top.
Never, never have you been so full,
overflowing with renewed energy!

163

From the abyss to the summit.
You find yourself full again, really full
since dancing the same step the air keeps rushing in,
making you overflow with joy, with energy.
Why should you be afraid of the bottom of the sea?
Together with the outward breath,
down you go
diving with the next wave
trying to plumb the depths.
And so you sail on
you go
from one contraction to the next
riding the waves
dancing with the storm.

165

Keeping them together,
the hand, the mind, the breath
what a problem, what a task.
But it happens.
They become one
spontaneously.
Not you but rhythm is leading the dance.
It is not your doing.
It merely happens.
Passive you are. Yet fully there.
Let your eye go astray,
your mind wander away
and the magic is gone.
If for a split second you stop and think
trying to remember the password
you are finished.
Get out of rhythm
even for just one breath
the tiger catches you!

These two, who are they?

– Man and woman.

– Yes, of course. But . . .?

– Lovers.

– Indeed.
  Two
  who cannot part.
  So close to one another that wherever one goes
  the other one follows.
  Their names?

– Juliet and Romeo
  Dante and Berenice
  Orpheus, Eurydice.

– A pair even more perfect?

– There is none.

– Of course, there is.

– Then who? Or where? Or in what time?

– Here and now.
  The two halves of your breath!
  You exhale.
  And sure enough, inhale follows.
  One dies?
  The other one must go.
  Two, who cannot part.
  As, indeed, everywhere.
  Since, wherever you look,
  always two are there.

High and low,
good and bad,
summer and winter,
night and day.
And since
two
means separation, means pain,
continuously, always, everywhere
two try to become one again.
What will they do?
Embrace one another
and dance.
— What of the two?
— Inhale, exhale?
  Continuously, infinitely
  they dance, don't they?
  And once in tune,
  once your breathing is right
  and full
  you feel as great, as big as life, don't you?
  Oh, yes, when you're happy, your breathing tells.
  Your voice is deep and strong.
  It resonates beautifully and tells
  how rooted you are, sure of yourself, having a core,
  at peace.
  If you are worried or in sorrow
  your voice becomes so thin that it can hardly be heard.
  It's a whisper.

And do you know
that our two lovers
can dance much more than just one step?
Who's the ballet master?
Our Lord, the Sun!
Day time.
You are awake, conscious as they say.
And so you communicate, you talk.
What is speech made of, please, tell me?
Your breath of course.
More precisely?
Exhale, exhale, exhale!
And, in between, inward breaths, that are so short, so modest
that they go unnoticed.
So much so that there seems to be
a continuous, unbroken, endless flux.

Sleep.
Night has taken the floor and is leading the dance.
You're there no more, as it were.
The submissive, ignored inhale takes revenge.
The slave now has the upper hand:
long, long, endless inward breaths.
So much so that, do you know what?
You snore.

And yet there's still another way
where neither rules nor obeys.
Inhale, exhale equal in strength,
in length.
Neither can say he rules.
Both play, both dance.
Both sing, one answering the other.
What sweet music.
A sorrow, a blessing?
Your heart's longing.
'I want', 'I do',
all that is gone
as is your petty will.
You have gladly surrendered to a power greater than you.
A prisoner, a slave are you
and yet, even the king envies you.
What is this blessed state, tell me,
where the crushing burden of choice
is suddenly lifted from your weary shoulders?
Love!
Exhale, inhale answering one another.
Crying, raving?
Or is it ecstasy?
No one can tell.
And probably it's both.
It is the song of man,
the breath, the song of life
you hear very late at night.

The wind is calling to the trees.
And the forest answers.
The sea is
making love to the shore
and the earth whispers
moaning in ecstasy.

10

reaching the harbour

Try to fill it up to the brim?
No, no. Never.
It would topple.
Better to have stopped in time.

Tao Te Ching

– May I still ask one more question?
– Of course. One, two, as many as you want.
– No. One. Just one.
  I think I know now how to use my breath during
  labour or, rather, how to flow with it and keep it
  constantly in harmony with the contractions. But please
  tell me how I am to use this breath when the time comes
  to push.
– To push?
– Yes. My friends told me that, at the end of labour,
  pushing the baby out can be really unbearable.

— Pushing out? Unbearable?
   Unbearable, what they so poetically call
   the last stage?
   Why! It ought to be the greatest time!
   You are reaching the culmination, the climax.
   How extraordinary that people can confuse and
   twist everything.
   Yes, I am afraid there's been a lot of confusion.
   And so, first of all, let us go back
   to what you're taught.

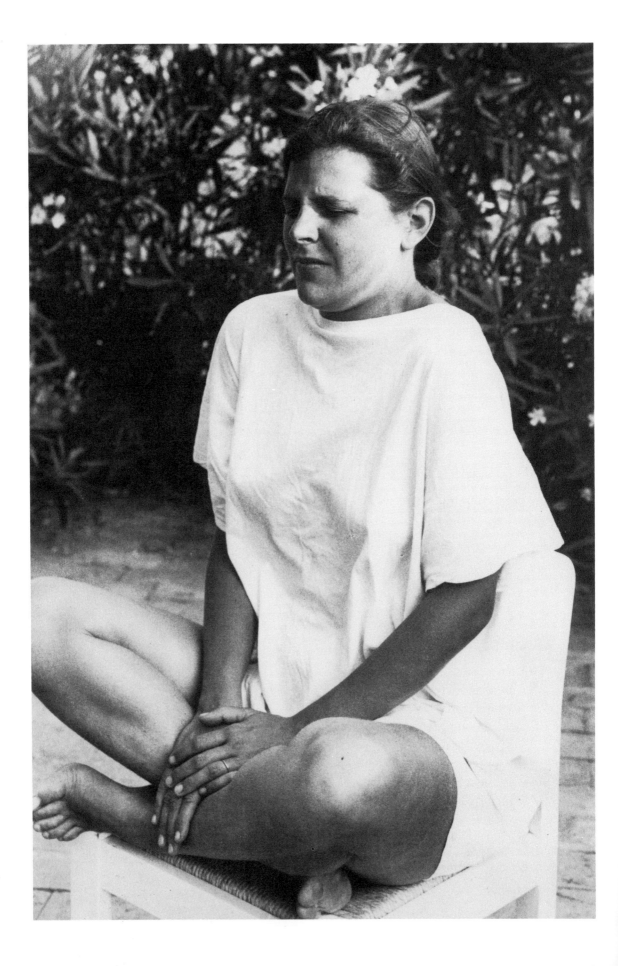

– Well, you remember, I told you,
   we're trained to . . . Why, to . . . take in air . . .!
– Yes. I remember you told me.
– The words are still ringing in my ears:
   "Breathe in! Take a deep breath!
   More! More! Hold it and
   push!!"
   Why! This is just the opposite of all you taught me!
   This is just what one ought not to do!
   Holding, blocking
   this is fighting, isn't it?
   Then, if you fight, how can you relax, let go!
   It's as good as telling you
   "Clench your teeth and smile."
   And, do you know what?
   We are supposed to take this air in
   with our chest.
– Well, it's all hard to believe.
   No wonder the results so rarely come up to
   the expectations.

179

"*Mater Dolorosa*
In pain shall ye give birth."
When you are applying all your energy,
all your strength
in the wrong direction
what else can you expect
but pain, suffering!

– "Push! Push! Harder! Harder!"
  Where do you see relaxation, here?
  Poor women.
  All they are pushing, is blood into their poor heads,
  with their poor swollen faces turning from red to blue,
  with tears rolling from their bloodshot eyes
  telling of their despair.
  Yes, poor women.
  With the feeling that they are getting nowhere although
  they are trying so hard, they turn mad, they turn hysterical.
  And do you know what?
  When they ought to be immersed in the rapture of love,
  reaching closer and closer to its culmination,
  towards its climax,
  do you know what they're told?
  "Harder! Harder! As if you're going to the toilet!"
– To . . . the toilet!
– Yes. To the toilet.
  However high you were, that would certainly bring
  you crashing to the ground.

– Enough! Enough!
   It's not surprising that the poor women get nowhere
   except frustrated and furious?
   Which justified anger, unfortunately, they're only
   too likely to turn upon the poor, innocent child!
– So let me see clearly how to use my breath at this
   crucial point. Please, teach me, tell me.
– I'm going to tell you.
   How to use the breath? No.
   How to flow with it, let it carry you.
   Yes to flow with it. Just as, in love, you let
   go and flow.
– In love, did you say? At the end of . . . labour?
– It's been the work of love all along!
   Haven't you recognised the rhythm?
   These waves that take you further and further,
   higher and higher until you reach . . . there!
– Oh! . . . Now that you tell me, of course, it's obvious.
– In love, try harder and harder and never will
   it happen. Never will you reach . . . there.
   And so, don't forget: it's not something you do
   with your body, it can't be a technique.
   You enter a rhythm. It is an art.
   You see, you are, as it were, at the end of a great
   drama. You are like a singer at the close of an opera.
   Shall we go back to the storm? Listen carefully.
   You've been sailing through powerful, at times
   angry waters.
   It seems you've reached the harbour, the land
   is close at hand, you feel you could almost
   touch it.

And then,
something very strange happens
the wind drops
the rage of the sea subsides
the contractions stop completely.
And it all becomes very quiet.
Quiet, yes, but the feeling is strange.
Not to say, uncanny.
The tiger roams unseen.
It is a point of complete, deep mystery.
Out of time and space.
The complete standstill just before you reach orgasm.
Out of space and time, yes.
You don't know really where you are.
And, possibly, you're there no more but gone
gone to meet the child
wherever it comes from.
For those who are there to help you,
obstetricians, midwives,
it seems nothing is happening.
They miss the depth, the sacredness of the moment.
Rather, their own suppressed fears, now, surface
and they begin to panic.
With the treacherous excuse
"What if anything happens to the child!"
they start doing all sorts of unwanted, foolish things
not for your sake but
to silence the anguish in their own hearts.

It's not their fault. They mean well.
But they don't know.
Certainly they have an excuse
they have never had the courage to set out on the journey
and taste the void.
They know nothing of the no man's land
that stretches between here
and there
and lies at the end of your breath.
Unable to follow where you've gone
they can't bear it.
Feeling you are beyond their reach,
they try to pull you back,
little knowing you to be
in another world
where you cannot be touched.
It takes courage, great courage to venture
into this no man's land of coming and going
of meeting and parting
being born and dying.
As for you, in this great adventure which is labour,
you come back, you've decided to stay
together with the gift you've been given.
And what is it
that will carry this hesitant boat ashore?
The storm, of course.

186

And here it comes again, raging, raving.
Tiger was not asleep
but only building up more anger.
The waves are now bigger, higher than ever,
as high, indeed, and frightening as huge mountains.
And, in between, dark, menacing, fathomless valleys.

– But, I
    shall not fear
    since you're going to tell me
    how to use my breath
    when it is all blowing, bellowing
    and the end is in sight?

187

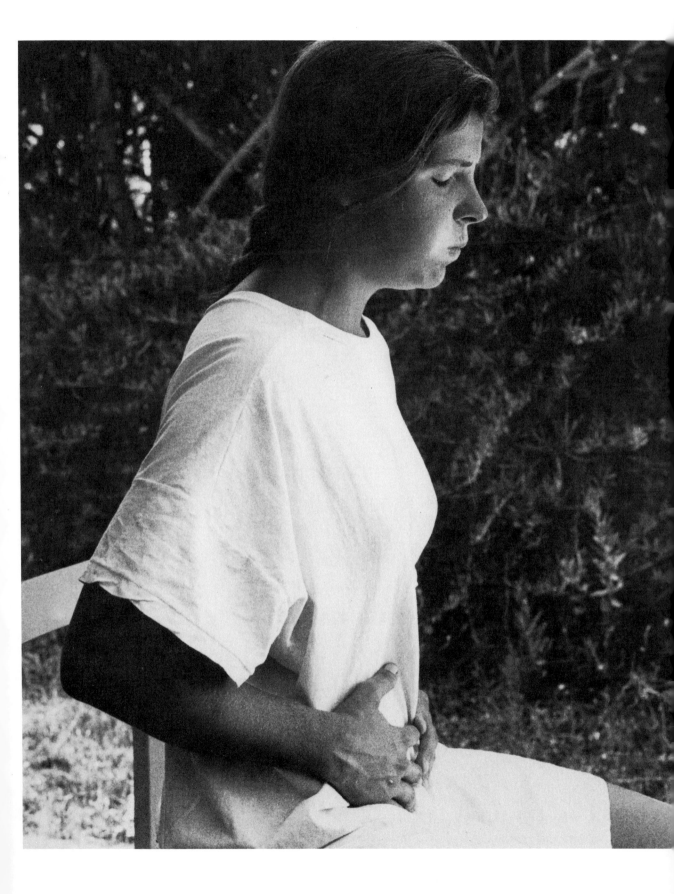

– Of course I am going to tell you.
   But, first, you tell me how do
   you
   see it.
– If I've understood you,
   if I can call myself your worthy disciple,
   since one is not to interfere with the breath
   but flow with it
   even at this point all that is to be done
   is to keep exhaling?
– Yes! How well you understand everything.
   Out, out, letting the air out
   making sure that the breathing is in perfect tune
   in harmony with the contraction, the wave.
   And in order to make the breath even more gentle
   you keep your lips close together and blow
   as if blowing out a candle.
   But be careful, don't hold your lips tight.
   Your mouth must remain very relaxed, very soft
   and your cheeks must fill up.
   Their bulging out will be the test and show
   that the lower part of your face is fully relaxed
   as will automatically be its counterpart
   the lower part of your body.

189

– I am afraid I feel a little silly, blowing like
  that and making such a face.
– Giacomella! Now, come on. You ought to know better.
– You're right. And I must say, this way of blowing
  does make the breath so gentle, so quiet.
  I feel I could make it last forever.
  And I feel even more peaceful.
  But . . .

– But?
– You still have not answered my question.
– Have I not?
  I think I told you everything.
  Of course you did not expect me
  to tell you what position, what posture …
  It's love we are talking about.
  Which is to say, the heart.
  While thinking of positions, postures, this
  is again the mind.
  Therefore, simply,
  no.
  Just surrender and let
  your inspiration
  tell you where to go.

– That wasn't my question.
– No? Then, what?
– If I'm so relaxed, I won't push?
– Push?
– And unless I push, and push very, very hard, how
 will the child be born?
– Is that what you think?
– Well . . . yes.
– Then, once again, you've got it all wrong.
– Am I not to push?
– Who likes to be pushed?
 Who wants to be shown the door, be kicked out?
 When your landlord throws you out, are you happy?
 Push the baby out?
 Is it an animal you force out of its den?
 Or a tree you shake madly to make it give up a fruit
 that's not ready?
 Push the child and make it fall?
 Nonsense!
 Push?
 No, no, never.

196

– Do you mean . . . that one is . . . not to push?
– You are not.
– I . . . don't push?
– You don't.
– But then, how shall I make the baby come out!
– You don't make it.
– I don't?

– You don't make the baby come out.
   You can't force it.
   You let it go, let it be born,
   let it leave you.
   You do not push. It pushes.
   You do not make efforts, struggle,
   you open up
   and surrender and flow
   and let the all powerful
   tide
   of breath, of love
   carry you both
   to the shore.
   How is the baby to be born?
   Like a whisper, like a smile,
   like the deep sigh that comes
   with the rapture of love's ecstasy.
   How many times am I to tell you
   you are in love, in love, in love
   immersed in the boundless sea
   of life, of love, of light
   the great ocean of infinite energy!

farewell

My publisher made me promise
"No poetry, this time.
People want facts."
I did promise.
But I could not resist.
The words of Socrates were in my ears.
"As for the great mysteries
don't talk about them unless
inspired
by the Muses
unless these heavenly damsels
are willing to whisper the answers in your ear.
Not with your logical, rational mind
but in a kind of delirium, a sort of madness
sent by the Gods
can one
at this gate enter."
These Gods! These Gods!
Is it my fault if poetry
is the only language they speak?

203

1

Said Fire:
– Among all of you, Gods,
    I am strongest.
    Water,
    I make you boil
    or even do away with you,
    turn you into vapour.
    Therefore, I shall expect that all of you
    shall bow to Me,
    your Lord.

2

– You fool! retorted Water vehemently.
    I
    put you out when I please.
    You, the stronger?
    But you'd be lost without me!
    Who else can quench your thirst,
    cool your anger,
    soothe your fever
    tell me,
    you, angry, silly, unhappy,
    clamorous child!

204

3

Once they saw
that neither could have the upper hand,
they got married.

Which, of course, did not put an end
to their strife.

4

Then, said the Wind:
– I,
and no one else,
am your master.
Flame
I blow you out when I please.
Sea,
the moment I open my mouth
you lose your temper
and look like a monster.
Therefore
to Me
both of you will obey.

5

In order to demonstrate his power
the Wind started blowing in a passion
as if drunk with his own might.
Then, seeing that violence, arrogance
took him nowhere
he made himself gentle.
Nothing but the sweetest of all sounds
was to be heard.
At times a buzzing swarm of bees,
at times a soft, tender, wailing whisper.

6

At this the two others
the two lovers
got really wild.
Fire
beaming, turned into pure
Light.
Water
shivered, quivered
and split
into millions and millions of dew drops
that kept glistening, sparkling
telling
of her long expected surrender
to her lover
her conquerer.

7

As for the Wind, he could be heard
as so many birds madly chippering, twittering
celebrating
the blest union
the joy of dawn
the birth of a new day
the glory of the whole
creation!